ROBERT SCHUMANN

SYMPHONY No. 4

D minor/d-Moll/Ré mineur
Op. 120
Edited by/Herausgegeben von
Linda Correll Roesner

T0080493

Ernst Eulenburg Ltd

London · Mainz · Madrid · New York · Paris · Tokyo · Toronto · Zürich

CONTENTS/INHALT

PREFACE/VORWORT

In 1853, when the first edition of Schumann's Symphony No. 4 in D minor, Op. 120 appeared, the publisher – or, more likely, Schumann himself – felt it necessary to call attention to the period of time that had elapsed between the work's composition and its publication. The verso of the score's title-page contains the following remark:

This symphony was sketched already in 1841, shortly after the first [symphony] in B flat major; however, it was not fully orchestrated until 1851. This comment seemed necessary since later two other symphonies appeared, designated Nos. 2 and 3; chronologically speaking, therefore, these would be the third and fourth.

Schumann's 'symphony year' of 1841 began with a flurry of activity on 23 January with his sketch of the B flat major symphony Op. 38 (the 'Spring'). This work, drafted in only four days and scored during the month of February, was performed as early as 31 March in a concert at the Leipzig Gewandhaus conducted by Mendelssohn. Its huge success was an immediate inspiration for Schumann to write, in April, another symphonic work (later published as 'Overture Scherzo and Finale' Op. 52). A fantasy for piano and orchestra (later to become the first movement of the Piano Concerto, Op. 54) followed in May. Schumann then turned to the composition of yet another symphony, in D minor. A degree of uncertainty, however, seems to have surrounded this work from its conception. According to Schumann's annotation in his *Haushaltbuch*, a household-accounts book that also served as an abbreviated diary, he

Als 1853 die Erstausgabe von Schumanns Sinfonie Nr. 4 in d-Moll op. 120 veröffentlicht wurde, schien es dem Verleger angebracht – wahrscheinlicher aber noch Schumann selbst –, auf die Zeitspanne hinzuweisen, die zwischen Komposition und Veröffentlichung dieses Werkes verstrichen war. In der Partitur findet sich auf der Rückseite des Titelblatts folgender Hinweis:

„Die Skizze dieser Symphonie entstand bereits im J. 1841 kurz nach der 1(sten) in B-Dur; wurde aber erst im J. 1851 vollständig instrumentirt. Diese Bemerkung schien nöthig, da später noch zwei mit den Nummern II und III bezeichnete Symphonien erschienen sind, die der Zeit der Entstehung nach folglich die III(te) und IV(te) wären."

Sein „Sinfoniejahr" 1841 begann Robert Schumann am 23. Januar mit fieberhafter Aktivität über den Skizzen zur B-Dur-Sinfonie op. 38, der *Frühlingssinfonie*. Dieses Werk, entworfen in nur vier Tagen und im Februar instrumentiert, wurde schon am 31. März in einem Konzert im Leipziger Gewandhaus unter Mendelssohns Leitung uraufgeführt. Der außerordentliche Erfolg dieser Sinfonie inspirierte den Komponisten schon im April zu einer weiteren sinfonischen Komposition, die später als Ouvertüre, Scherzo und Finale op. 52 veröffentlicht wurde. Eine Phantasie für Klavier und Orchester folgte im Mai und wurde später zum ersten Satz des Klavierkonzerts op. 54. Danach wandte sich Schumann einer weiteren Sinfonie zu mit der Tonart d-Moll. Ein gewisses Maß an Unsicherheit scheint dieses Werk aber von Anfang an umgeben zu haben. Folgt man seinem *Haushaltbuch*, das auch als stich-

began the work on 29 May 1841.[1] But on 9 June, before he had finished his sketch, he – uncharacteristically – set it aside. Returning to it on 1 August, Schumann finished the draft. The task of revising his B flat major symphony for publication, however, prevented him from resuming work on the D minor şymphony until the end of the month. He completed the orchestration of the first movement on 31 August and of the entire symphony on 9 September (both of these dates appear in the 1841 autograph score as well as in the *Haushaltbuch*). On 13 September 1841, Clara Schumann's 22nd birthday and the day after Robert and Clara Schumann's first wedding anniversary, Schumann surprised his wife with the completed score of the D minor symphony, the first printed orchestral parts (proof sheets) of the B flat major symphony, and the newly-printed Rückert Lieder, Op. 37.[2]

Later that year, on 6 December, the D minor symphony had its first performance at the Leipzig Gewandhaus in a concert given by Clara Schumann with Franz Liszt as guest artist. Ferdinand David conducted. Apparently the symphony was not well played. Moreover, its reception was overshadowed by the furore surrounding the performance of Liszt's *Hexameron* by the two virtuoso pianists.[3] After this less-than-auspicious première Schumann did not actively seek another performance. Apart from a halfhearted attempt in the au-

[1] Robert Schumann, *Tagebücher*, Band III, *Haushaltbücher*, ed. Gerd Nauhaus (Leipzig, 1982), p. 184. The *Haushaltbuch* is the source for all of the dates cited in the present discussion.

[2] Both Robert and Clara Schumann's accounts of this day are preserved in their *Ehetagebuch*. Robert Schumann, *Tagebücher*, Band II, *1836–1854*, ed. Gerd Nauhaus (Leipzig, 1987), pp. 185–186. English translation in *The Marriage Diaries of Robert & Clara Schumann*, ed. Gerd Nauhaus, transl. Peter Ostwald (Boston, 1993), pp. 108–109.

[3] Clara Schumann's account of the event in the *Ehetagebuch* is revealing. ibid., p. 195. English transl., pp. 120–121.

wortartiges Tagebuch diente, so begann er mit dieser Komposition am 29. Mai 1841[1]. Aber schon am 9. Juni legte er die Skizzen wieder beiseite, bevor er sie beendet hatte; das war sehr ungewöhnlich für Schumann. Am 1. August nahm er sie sich wieder vor und schloß den Entwurf ab. Die Aufgabe, die B-Dur-Sinfonie für die Veröffentlichung durchzusehen, hielt ihn jedoch von der Arbeit an der d-Moll-Sinfonie bis zum Ende des Monats ab. Am 31. August beendete er die Instrumentation des ersten Satzes und am 9. September der gesamten Sinfonie. Diese beiden Daten finden sich in der autographen Partitur von 1841 und auch im *Haushaltbuch*. Am 13. September 1841, Claras 22. Geburtstag und einen Tag nach Robert und Clara Schumanns erstem Hochzeitstag, überraschte der Komponist seine Frau mit der Partitur der d-Moll-Sinfonie, den ersten Korrekturabzügen der Orchesterstimmen der B-Dur-Sinfonie und mit den frisch gedruckten *Rückert-Liedern* op. 37.[2]

Später im selben Jahr, am 6. Dezember, wurde die d-Moll-Sinfonie im Leipziger Gewandhaus in einem Konzert uraufgeführt, das Clara Schumann und Franz Liszt als Gast mitgestalteten. Ferdinand David dirigierte. Allem Anschein nach war die Darbietung mäßig. Darüber hinaus stellte das Aufsehen, das der Vortrag von Liszts *Hexameron* durch die beiden Klaviervirtuosen erregte, die Aufnahme der Sinfonie in den Schatten.[3] Nach der alles andere als vielversprechenden Premiere hat Schumann sich nicht sonderlich um eine weitere Auf-

[1] *Robert Schumann, Tagebücher*, Band III, *Haushaltbücher*, hg. von Gerd Nauhaus, Leipzig 1982, S. 184. Das *Haushaltbuch* ist Grundlage für alle im weiteren zitierten Daten.

[2] Die Darstellungen von Robert und Clara Schumann sind in ihrem *Ehetagebuch* festgehalten. *Robert Schumann, Tagebücher*, Band II, 1836–1854, hg. von Gerd Nauhaus, Leipzig 1987, S. 185f.

[3] Aufschlußreich ist Clara Schumanns Bericht über dieses Ereignis im *Ehetagebuch*; ebda., S. 195.

tumn of 1843 to interest the publishing firm of C. F. Peters in the work,[4] the composer appears to have abandoned it. Then, on 12 December 1851, almost exactly 10 years after the disappointing première, Schumann took up the D minor symphony again. What might his reasons have been for returning to the work?

One of the most striking features of the D minor symphony is its structure. The individual movements – none of them entirely complete in themselves – are intended to follow one another without breaks, resulting in a large one-movement design. Common thematic, rhythmic, and harmonic threads run through the work. In 1841 such an approach to symphonic form was unusual.[5] It was, of course, to become popular during the second half of the 19th century, when the aesthetic ideal of the total unification of a work of art would dominate creative thinking.

Perhaps it was Schumann's own engagement with this aesthetic ideal in his late works that led to a resumption of interest in the abandoned symphony.[6] In any event, Schumann completed the new score on 19 December. The original title-page and the first page of musical text of the 1851 autograph score reveal that the composer considered re-titling the work 'Phantasie' (he also refers to it once in the *Haushaltbuch* as 'Phantasie'). Although some of the revisions Schumann made in 1851 are substantial, the style of the symphony re-

4 See Rufus Hallmark, 'The Sketches for *Dichterliebe*', *19th-Century Music*, I (1977), p. 133
5 See the press reviews of the concert of 6 December 1841 reproduced in Egon Voss, 'Einführung und Analyse', in the Goldman-Schott *Taschenpartitur* of the symphony (Mainz, 1980), pp. 147–148
6 See Linda Correll Roesner, 'Ästhetisches Ideal und symphonische Gestalt: Die d-moll-Symphonie um die Jahrhundertmitte', in *Schumann in Düsseldorf. Werke – Texte – Interpretationen*, ed. Bernhard R. Appel (Mainz, 1993), pp. 55–71

führung bemüht. Abgesehen von einem halbherzigen Versuch im Herbst 1843, den Verlag C. F. Peters für eine Veröffentlichung zu gewinnen[4], scheint der Komponist dieses Werk abgeschrieben zu haben. Am 12. Dezember 1851 dann, fast genau 10 Jahre nach der enttäuschenden Uraufführung, wendete sich Schumann der d-Moll-Sinfonie wieder zu. Was mögen seine Gründe gewesen sein, auf dieses Werk zurückzukommen?

Eines seiner bemerkenswertesten Kennzeichen ist der Aufbau. Die einzelnen Sätze – keiner von ihnen in sich selbst wirklich abgeschlossen – sollen einander ohne Pause folgen und führen so zu einer großen einsätzigen Faktur. Gemeinsame thematische, rhythmische und harmonische Zusammenhänge durchziehen das Werk. Im Jahr 1841 war diese Annäherung an die sinfonische Form noch ungewöhnlich.[5] Freilich sollte sie dann in der zweiten Hälfte des 19. Jahrhunderts weit verbreitet sein, in der das ästhetische Ideal der vollständigen Vereinheitlichung eines Kunstwerkes das kreative Denken beherrschte.

Vielleicht war es Schumanns Verantwortungsgefühl gegenüber seinem Spätwerk, das sein Interesse an der aufgegebenen Sinfonie wieder weckte[6]. Wie auch immer: Am 19. Dezember 1851 beendete er die neue Partitur, deren Deckblatt und die erste Notenseite darauf hinweisen, daß der Komponist das Werk in „Phantasie" umbenennen wollte. (Auch im *Haushaltbuch* findet sich ein entsprechender Bezug.) Sind die Änderungen Schumanns von 1851 auch tiefgreifend, so bleibt die Anlage der Sinfonie von 1841 in ihrer Substanz doch

4 vgl. Rufus Hallmark, „The Sketches for *Dichterliebe*", in: *19th-Century Music* I (1977), S. 133
5 vgl. die Rezension dieses Konzertes, das am 6. Dezember 1841 stattfand; zitiert in: *Robert Schumann. Sinfonie Nr. 4 d-Moll op. 120.* Einführung und Analyse von Egon Voss, München-Mainz 1980, S. 147f.
6 vgl. Linda Correll Roesner, „Ästhetisches Ideal und symphonische Gestalt: Die d-moll-Symphonie um die Jahrhundertmitte", in *Schumann in Düsseldorf. Werke – Texte – Interpretationen*, hg. von Bernhard R. Appel, Mainz 1993, S. 55–71

mained essentially that of 1841. In this regard it is interesting to note that Schumann's comments in the *Haushaltbuch* and in the 1851 autograph score show that he thought of his revision principally in terms of orchestration (see Editorial Notes below).

Stylistically, the music Schumann composed in the 1850s had moved considerably beyond his works of the early 1840s, a point not lost on reviewers of the first performances of the symphony in its revised version.[7] The tendency towards tonal synthesis,[8] the dense textures, the marked slowing of the harmonic rhythm coupled with a leaning towards rapidly moving, almost rhapsodic melodic lines, the increased rhythmic flexibility – in short, all of the hallmarks of Schumann's late style that lend breadth and continuity to the music – are foreign to the works of the early 1840s. Is it possible that, after having 'modernized' the orchestration, Schumann was worried that the heavier scoring characteristic of his musical thinking in 1851 might be incompatible with music he had composed in 1841? Some such concern about the symphony's viability may have made him cautious in committing himself fully to it for, although he had a set of orchestral parts copied early in 1852, he seems to have been hesitant about bringing the work to performance. No further mention of the symphony appears in any of the primary sources until 30 December 1852, when Schumann noted in the *Haushaltbuch* that he had completed a 4-hand piano arrangement.

The first performance of the 1851 version finally took place in Düsseldorf on 3 March 1853, with Schumann conducting. His comment in the *Haushaltbuch* – '*Dmoll*symphonie [sic] u. Freude daran' ('D minor symphony and joy in it')[9] – indi-

erhalten. In dieser Hinsicht kommen Schumanns Notizen im *Haushaltbuch* und in der Partitur von 1851 insofern Bedeutung zu, als er darauf hinweist, im wesentlichen an eine Neuinstrumentierung gedacht zu haben (siehe Einzelanmerkungen unten).

In stilistischer Hinsicht haben sich Schumanns Werke der fünfziger Jahre beträchtlich über die der Vierziger hinaus entwickelt. Dies entging auch den Rezensenten der Uraufführung der überarbeiteten Fassung nicht.[7] Die Tendenz zur tonartlichen Geschlossenheit[8], die dichte Textur, die auffallende Verlangsamung des harmonischen Rhythmus gepaart mit einer Neigung zu rasch-bewegten, beinahe rhapsodischen melodischen Linien, die gesteigerte rhythmische Flexibilität – kurz: all die Zeichen von Schumanns Spätstil, die seiner Musik Weite und inneren Zusammenhang verleihen, sind den Werken der frühen 1840er Jahre fremd. Ist es denkbar, daß Schumann nach der „modernisierten" Orchestrierung besorgt war, seine die musikalische Denkart der Jahres 1851 bezeichnende „schwere" Instrumentierung könne mit der 1841 komponierten Musik nicht vereinbar sein? Etwas von einer solchen Sorge über die Überlebensfähigkeit der Sinfonie könnte mit der Grund dafür gewesen sein, sich so wenig für das Werk einzusetzen. Zwar ließ er Anfang 1852 die Stimmen abschreiben, zögerte aber dennoch, das Werk aufführen zu lassen. Erst am 30. Dezember 1852 wird die Sinfonie in den Primärquellen wieder erwähnt, als Schumann im *Haushaltbuch* notierte, er habe einen Klavierauszug zu vier Händen fertiggestellt.

Schumann selbst dirigierte schließlich die Uraufführung der Fassung von 1851 am 3. März 1853 in Düsseldorf. Seine Eintragungen im *Haushaltbuch* – „*Dmoll*symphonie u. Freude daran"[9] – zeugen vom Erfolg der Aufführung. Wenig später ver-

---

[7] See the reviews cited in Voss, op. cit., pp. 155 ff.

[8] See Reinhard Kapp, *Studien zum Spätwerk Robert Schumanns* (Tutzing, 1984), especially pp. 168–178

[9] *Tagebücher*, Band III, *Haushaltbücher*, op. cit., p. 618

[7] vgl. die Rezensionen in Egon Voss, a. a. O., S. 155ff.

[8] vgl. Reinhard Kapp, *Studien zum Spätwerk Robert Schumanns*, Tutzing 1984, besonders S. 168–178

[9] *Tagebücher*, Band III, *Haushaltbücher*, a. a. O., S. 618

cates that the performance was a success. Shortly thereafter he sold the symphony to the publishers Breitkopf & Härtel, receiving 36 Louis d'or for it on 6 May.[10] An unpublished letter of 21 April 1853 from Breitkopf & Härtel to Schumann contains details of the publishing agreement.[11] They promised him multiple engraved copies of the string parts by 11 May, in time for a performance of the symphony at the Niederrheinisches Musikfest in Cologne on 15 May. Schumann had requested these string parts in a letter of 18 April and apparently had also raised the question of the symphony's numbering at that time, for the publisher's letter firmly states that the symphony must be given the number four and the opus number 120. Perhaps this exchange about the symphony's numbering offers another indication that Schumann was somewhat uncomfortable with the style of the work and did not want the public to perceive it as one of his newest creations. Although Schumann's letter to Breitkopf & Härtel of 18 April 1853 is no longer extant, it is not difficult to surmise from the reply that the composer had wished to number the symphony in accordance with its chronological position (i.e., as Symphony No 2; see also the remark on the verso of the titlepage of the first edition cited above). A letter Schumann wrote to Johann Verhulst on 3 May 1853, less than two weeks before the symphony was scheduled to be performed at the Niederrheinisches Musikfest, provides another indication of his ambivalence.[12] Turns of phrase such as 'the old symphony' and 'it is almost against my will that it be performed', coupled with Schumann's observation that he had in any event completely re-orchestrated the work, strongly suggest he was keenly aware that stylis-

kaufte er die Sinfonie an das Verlagshaus Breitkopf & Härtel und erhielt dafür am 6. Mai 36 Louis d'or[10]. Ein unveröffentlichter Brief von Breitkopf & Härtel an Schumann, datiert mit 21. April 1853, teilt Einzelheiten der Abmachung für die Veröffentlichung mit.[11] So garantierten sie ihm zum 11. Mai, rechtzeitig zu einer Aufführung der Sinfonie anläßlich des Niederrheinischen Musikfestes in Köln am 15. Mai, einen Stimmensatz der Streicher in mehrfacher Ausfertigung. In einem Brief vom 18. April hatte Schumann diese Streicherstimmen erbeten und bei dieser Gelegenheit augenscheinlich auch die Frage nach der Zählung der Sinfonie zur Sprache gebracht; der Brief des Verlegers nämlich bestimmt die Nummer 4 und die Opuszahl 120. Dieser Gedankenaustausch über die Numerierung der Sinfonie bringt vielleicht einen weiteren Aspekt ins Spiel: Schumann fühlte sich bei der Kompositionsweise des Werks unbehaglich und wünschte nicht, daß man es für eine seiner neuesten Schöpfungen hielt. Wenn auch sein Brief vom 18. April 1853 an Breitkopf & Härtel sich nicht erhalten hat, kann man doch unschwer aus dem Antwortbrief ablesen, daß der Komponist eine Numerierung der Sinfonie gewünscht hatte, die chronologisch korrekt war (folglich als Sinfonie Nr. 2; vergleiche hierzu die Anmerkung auf der Rückseite des Titelblattes der Erstausgabe, die weiter oben zitiert wurde). Ein Brief an Johann Verhulst vom 3. Mai 1853, weniger als zwei Wochen vor der angekündigten Aufführung beim Niederrheinischen Musikfest geschrieben, sorgt für ein weiteres Indiz für Schumanns zwiespältige Haltung[12]. Formulierungen wie „die alte Symphonie" und „es ist beinahe gegen meinen Willen, daß sie aufgeführt wird" im Verein mit sei-

[10] ibid., p. 681
[11] Kraków, Biblioteka Jagiellońska, No. 4686 in Band 25 of Schumann's correspondence; copy in Robert-Schumann-Forschungsstelle, Düsseldorf

[12] *Robert Schumann's Briefe. Neue Folge*, ed. F. Gustav Jansen, 2nd ed. (Leipzig, 1904), pp. 371–372

[10] ebda., S. 681
[11] Krakau, Biblioteka Jagiellońska, Nr 4686 in Band 25 von Schumanns Korrespondenz; eine Kopie befindet sich in der Robert-Schumann-Forschungsstelle, Düsseldorf

[12] *Robert Schumanns Briefe. Neue Folge*, hg. von Gustav Jansen, Leipzig (2)1904, S. 371f.

tically he no longer spoke the symphony's language. But the symphony was well received at the musical festival, and with this success Schumann appears to have cast his reservations aside.

A comment on the 1841 version of the symphony seems appropriate. Its first champion was Johannes Brahms, whose extensive collection of MSS included Schumann's 1841 autograph score. Brahms's love for the early version and his conviction that its fresh beauty and gracefulness had been lost in the 'ponderous dress' of Schumann's 1851 orchestration[13] led him to undertake, together with the conductor Franz Wüllner, an edition of the 1841 version. This edition, published in 1891 by Breitkopf & Härtel as a supplement to the Schumann *Gesamtausgabe* (Series I, No. IVa), is actually a conflation of the 1841 and 1851 versions. In 1982 C. F. Peters published an edition by the conductor Marc Andreae. A critical edition of the 1841 version is planned as part of the new Schumann *Gesamtausgabe*.

Editorial Notes

The sources for the D minor symphony are incomplete. Apart from a few brief sketches on the verso of a song MS,[14] and an even briefer sketch – one that postdates the composition of the symphony – in Schumann's

---

ner Bemerkung, er habe die Sinfonie allenfalls völlig uminstrumentiert, zeugen eindeutig von seinem klaren Bewußtsein, die Sprache dieser Sinfonie schon längst nicht mehr zu sprechen. Doch fand die Sinfonie auf dem Musikfest eine gute Aufnahme, und über diesem Erfolg sind Schumanns Bedenken offenbar geschwunden.

Eine Anmerkung über die Fassung der Sinfonie von 1841 scheint hier angebracht: Ihr erster Fürsprecher war Johannes Brahms, in dessen umfangreicher Sammlung von Manuskripten sich auch die autographe 1841er Partitur befand. Brahms gab der Urfassung eindeutig den Vorzug, und aufgrund seiner Überzeugung, deren erfrischende Schönheit und Feinheit seien im „schwerfälligen Kleid" der Instrumentierung von 1851 untergegangen[13], brachte er in Zusammenarbeit mit dem Dirigenten Franz Wüllner eine Ausgabe der Fassung von 1841 heraus. Sie erschien 1891 als Supplement zur Gesamtausgabe bei Breitkopf & Härtel (Serie I, Nr. IVa) und stellt eher eine Mischform der Fassungen von 1841 und 1851 dar. C. F. Peters veröffentlichte 1982 eine Ausgabe des Dirigenten Marc Andreae. Eine Kritische Ausgabe der Fassung von 1841 im Rahmen der Schumann-Gesamtausgabe steht derzeit an.

Revisionsbericht

Die Quellen der d-Moll-Sinfonie sind unvollständig. Über wenige Skizzen auf der Rückseite eines Liedmanuskripts[14] hinaus sowie einer noch knapperen Skizze in Schumanns Reisetagebuch vom Jahre

---

13 See Brahms's letter of late December 1889 to Franz Wüllner, in *Johannes Brahms Briefwechsel*, XV, *Johannes Brahms im Briefwechsel mit Franz Wüllner*, ed. Ernst Wolf (Berlin, 1921; reprint Tutzing, 1974), p. 167

14 Paris, Bibliothèque nationale, Mus. Ms. 342. See Rufus Hallmark, 'A Sketch Leaf for Schumann's D-Minor Symphony', *Mendelssohn and Schumann, Essays on Their Music and its Context*, ed. Jon. W. Finson and R. Larry Todd (Durham, NC, 1984), pp. 39–51.

13 vgl. den Brief von Brahms an Franz Wüllner von Ende Dezember 1889, in: *Johannes Brahms Briefwechsel*, XV, *Johannes Brahms im Briefwechsel mit Franz Wüllner*, hg. von Ernst Wolf, Berlin 1921, Reprint Tutzing 1974, S. 167

14 Paris, Bibliothèque nationale, Mus. Ms. 342. Vgl. Rufus Hallmark, „A Sketch Leaf for Schumann's D-minor-Symphony", in: *Mendelssohn and Schumann. Essays on Their Music and its Context*, hg. von Jon W. Finson und R. Larry Todd, Durham, NC, 1984, S. 39–51

travel diary of 1842,[15] no sketches or continuity draft of the symphony have survived. The *Stichvorlagen* (engraver's copy-texts) for the score and the orchestral parts of the first edition likewise have not survived. Fortunately Schumann's autograph scores of both the 1841 and 1851 versions of the symphony are extant. The 1841 autograph,[16] dated Leipzig, 9 September 1841, contains several layers of revision, the last of which dates from December 1851, when Schumann rewrote the symphony. Other revisions in this MS may have originated in October 1843, when Schumann offered the symphony along with several other works to the publishers C. F. Peters. In the preparation of the present edition the 1841 autograph score has been carefully collated. Its readings, however, have been taken into account only for the purposes of comparison and corroboration. The readings of the 4-hand piano arrangement prepared by Schumann in December 1852[17] have likewise been consulted for purposes of corroboration.

The following sources form the basis of the present edition:

1. Schumann's autograph score of the 1851 version of the symphony (AUT). Berlin, Staatsbibliothek zu Berlin – Preußischer Kulturbesitz, Mus. ms. autogr. Schumann 17. This score, completed in Düsseldorf on 19 December 1851, bore on its original title-page (now the last page of the MS) the title 'Symphonistische Phantasie' and on the first page of musical text the caption 'Fantasie für Orchester' (later changed to 'Symphonie für Orchester'). On 23 December 1853, after publication of the first edition, Schumann presented the MS to Joseph Joachim. A new title-page added at that time

1842[15] – in dem die Komposition der Sinfonie nachdatiert wird – sind keine Skizzen oder Entwürfe erhalten. Ebenfalls gibt es weder Stichvorlagen für Partitur noch Einzelstimmen der Erstausgabe. Glücklicherweise existieren die autographen Partituren der Sinfoniefassungen von 1841 und 1851. Das Autograph von 1841[16] mit Datum „Leipzig, 9. September 1841" offenbart verschiedene Überarbeitungsphasen der Sinfonie, deren letzte aus dem Dezember 1851 stammt. Im Zusammenhang mit einem Angebot der Sinfonie und weiterer Werke an C. F. Peters im Oktober 1843 hat Schumann wohl zusätzliche Änderungen vorgenommen. Die vorliegende Ausgabe ist unter sorgfältigem kritischen Vergleich mit der autographen Partitur von 1841 vorgenommen worden. Deren Lesarten sind allerdings lediglich zum Vergleich und zur Absicherung berücksichtigt. Zudem fand aus Gründen der Bestätigung ein Vergleich des von Schumann im Dezember 1852[17] erstellten Auszugs für Klavier zu vier Händen statt.

Folgende Quellen sind Grundlagen dieser Ausgabe:

1. Schumanns autographe Partitur der Sinfonie in der Fassung von 1851 (AUT). Berlin, Staatsbibliothek zu Berlin – Preußischer Kulturbesitz, Mus. ms. Autogr. Schumann 17. Sie wurde am 19. Dezember 1851 in Düsseldorf abgeschlossen und trug ursprünglich auf der Titelseite die Bezeichnung „Symphonistische Phantasie" und auf der ersten Notenseite die Überschrift „Fantasie für Orchester" (später abgeändert in „Symphonie für Orchester"). Nach Erscheinen der Erstausgabe am 23. Dezember 1853 überreichte Schumann das Autograph an Joseph Joachim. Das zu dieser Zeit hin-

---

[15] 'Reisenotizen V' (Hamburg, 1842), Zwickau, Robert-Schumann-Haus, 4871 VII A/b, 5 A3

[16] Vienna, Gesellschaft der Musikfreunde, A 292 (Nachlaß Brahms)

[17] Leipzig: Breitkopf & Härtel (November 1853), plate no. 8742; price: 2 Thlr

[15] *Reisenotizen V*, Hamburg 1842, Zwickau, Robert-Schumann-Haus, 4871 VII A/b, 5 A3

[16] Wien, Gesellschaft der Musikfreunde, A 292 (Nachlaß Brahms)

[17] Leipzig: Breitkopf & Härtel (November 1853), Plattennummer 8742, Preis 2 Thlr

X

designates the work as a symphony and contains the following dedication:

When the first sounds of this symphony emerged, Joseph Joachim was still a little boy; since then the symphony and particularly the boy have grown, so I also dedicate it to him – even though only in private.

The MS is written in a light-brown ink on printed 24-staff paper with an additional staff ruled with a rastrum at the top and at the bottom of each page (there are two orchestral systems per page). It contains additions and corrections in pencil and red pencil, as well as revisions in a dark ink and very fine pen point. The revisions in this dark ink appear to date from early in 1853, when Schumann was preparing the symphony for performance. The Romanze and the Scherzo are predominately in a copyist's hand, the musical text taken directly from the 1841 autograph (see below).

2. The first edition of the full score (1E). Leipzig: Breitkopf & Härtel [December 1853]; plate no. 8795; price; 4 Thlr. The wording of the title-page makes it very clear that the 'movements' of the symphony are to follow one another without breaks and that the work endeavors to project a single movement: 'Symphonie/No. IV. D moll/Introduction, Allegro, Romanze, Scherzo und Finale/in einem Satze/für grosses Orchester.' Two copies of the score were consulted: Washington, DC, Library of Congress; Vienna, Gesellschaft der Musikfreunde. The *Stichvorlage* (no longer extant) for 1E was presumably a MS in a copyist's hand copied from AUT early in 1853, shortly before the first performance of the symphony in its new version.

zugefügte Titelblatt bezeichnete das Werk als Sinfonie und trägt diese Widmung:

„Als die ersten Klänge dieser Symphonie entstanden, da war Joseph Joachim noch ein kleiner Bursch; seitdem ist die Symphonie und noch mehr der Bursch größer gewachsen, weshalb ich sie ihm auch, wenn auch nur im stillen – widme."

Das Autograph ist in hellbrauner Tinte auf gedrucktem 24zeiligen Notenpapier geschrieben; zusätzlich findet sich auf jeder Seite oben und unten gezeichnet je ein rastriertes zusätzliches System (bei zwei Akkoladen pro Seite). Es enthält Zusätze und Korrekturen mit Blei und in roter Tinte sowie auch Überarbeitungen mit dunkler Tinte und sehr feinem Stift. Die Änderungen in dieser dunklen Tinte haben ihren Ursprung offenbar in Schumanns Vorbereitungen auf die Aufführung Anfang 1853. Romanze und Scherzo stammen überwiegend von der Hand eines Kopisten, der Notentext ist vollständig aus der Handschrift von 1841 übernommen (siehe unten).

2. Erstausgabe der Partitur (1E). Leipzig, Breitkopf & Härtel [Dezember 1853]; Platten-Nummer 8795; Preis: 4 Thaler. Der Wortlaut des Titelblattes verdeutlicht, daß die Sätze der Sinfonie ohne Pause ineinander übergehen sollen und daß sie auf ein einsätziges Werk angelegt ist: „Symphonie/ No. IV. D moll/ Introduction, Allegro, Romanze, Scherzo und Finale/ in einem Satze/ für/ grosses Orchester". Zwei Exemplare der Partitur wurden für diese Ausgabe hinzugezogen: Library of Congress, Washington, DC; Gesellschaft der Musikfreunde, Wien. Die verschollene Stichvorlage zu 1E, so ist anzunehmen, hat ein Kopist Anfang 1853 anhand von AUT angefertigt, als die Erstaufführung der Neufassung der Sinfonie unmittelbar bevorstand.

3. The first edition of the orchestral parts (OP). Leipzig: Breitkopf & Härtel [November 1853]; plate no. 8735; price; 6 Thlr. Copy in Vienna, Gesellschaft der Musikfreunde (incomplete; lacking violin I, cello and double bass); copy in the private collection of Dr Kurt Hofmann, Lübeck. An annotation in Schumann's hand on the original title-page of the 1851 autograph (AUT) shows that he sent the score to a copyist on 26 December 1851. Unpublished letters to Schumann from Karl Gottschalk, the Dresden copyist who continued in his employ after Schumann's move from Dresden to Düsseldorf, indicate that it was Gottschalk who received the score and that he used it to prepare a set of orchestral parts.[18] This set of handwritten parts (no longer extant) evidently served later as *Stichvorlage* for OP. OP and IE differ in some details, and it is important to note that OP sometimes has readings that correspond to the original readings of AUT before Schumann's last (1853?) revision of the MS. This suggests that the no-longer-extant *Stichvorlage* for the full score was not copied until early 1853, that it incorporated the final layer of revision in AUT, and that the already-copied handwritten parts were not scrutinized during this late stage of the revision process.

As is evident from the above description of the sources, the gaps in the transmission of the D minor symphony constitute a considerable handicap to achieving a definitive musical text – a text that is not only accu-

3. Erstausgabe der Stimmen (OP). Leipzig, Breitkopf & Härtel (November 1853); Platten-Nummer 8735; Preis: 6 Thaler. Exemplar bei der Gesellschaft der Musikfreunde in Wien (die Stimmen von Violine I, Violoncello und Kontrabaß fehlen; ein Exemplar ist im Privatbesitz von Dr. Kurt Hofmann, Lübeck). Am 26. Dezember 1851 schickte Schumann die Partitur an einen Kopisten, wie seine handschriftliche Bemerkung auf dem Titelblatt des von 1851 stammenden Autographs (AUT) belegt. Laut unveröffentlichten Briefen Karl Gottschalks – er war Schumanns Kopist in Dresden und nach dessen Umsiedelung auch in Düsseldorf – handelte es sich dabei um ihn selbst, der nach Erhalt der Partitur die Stimmen anfertigte.[18] Dieser verschollene handgeschriebene Stimmensatz diente später offenbar als Stichvorlage für OP. OP und IE unterscheiden sich geringfügig; von Bedeutung ist, daß manche Lesarten in OP sich mit den ursprünglichen von AUT dekken, bevor Schumann, möglicherweise 1853, dort die letzten Änderungen anbrachte. So liegt also der Schluß nahe, daß die verschollene Stichvorlage der Partitur 1. erst Anfang 1853 entstand, 2. sie die letzte Schicht der Änderungen in AUT einschloß, und 3. die bereits herausgeschriebenen Stimmen gegen Ende dieses Überarbeitungsvorganges nicht genau geprüft wurden.

Diese Beschreibung der Quellenlage verdeutlicht, daß die Lücken in der Überlieferung der d-Moll-Sinfonie ein erhebliches Hindernis darstellen, zu einem endgültigen Notentext zu kommen – ein No-

---

[18] Gottschalk's letters to Schumann of 2 January 1852, undated [early February] 1852 (with an invoice), and 1 March 1852 are preserved in the Biblioteka Jagiellońska, Kraków (Band 24, Nos. 4376, 4453, 4436 of Schumann's correspondence). Copies were made available to me in the Robert-Schumann-Forschungsstelle, Düsseldorf. The 14 Thaler that Schumann sent Gottschalk on 5 March 1852 (*Haushaltbuch*, p. 588) were probably in payment for these orchestral parts.

[18] Die Briefe Gottschalks an Schumann vom 2. Januar 1852, ein undatierter von (Anfang) Februar 1852 und einer vom 1. März 1852 werden in der Biblioteka Jagiellońska in Krakau aufbewahrt (Band 24, Nr. 4376, 4453 und 4436 von Schumanns Korrespondenz). Kopien davon hat mir die Robert-Schumann-Forschungsstelle, Düsseldorf, zugänglich gemacht. Die 14 Taler, die Schumann am 5. März 1852 an Gottschalk schickte (*Haushaltbuch*, S. 588), waren vermutlich das Honorar für diese Kopie der Stimmen.

rate, but one that reflects Schumann's modes of expression and his aesthetic position. The absence of a *Stichvorlage* for the score is particularly unfortunate. Without this MS it is difficult to interpret the differences between AUT and 1E. AUT contains considerably more indications of expressive nuance than the 'regularized' 1E. The *Stichvorlage* – the missing link – would almost certainly provide clues as to how much of this nuance was lost in the copying process and how much was a result of the publisher's editorial policy and house style. (To judge from other *Stichvorlagen* in copyists' hands, the MS would have contained numerous emendations made by Schumann; many, possibly all, of the expression indications would also have been in Schumann's hand.)

The problem of achieving a definitive musical text is further complicated by the circumstances surrounding the origin of the 1851 version of the symphony. The new score (AUT) was completed in only eight days (12–19 December 1851), a short time even for a composer who habitually worked quickly. It seems clear that, once embarked on the revision, Schumann's prime concern was orchestration. In AUT he even referred several times to the 1841 score as a 'sketch': '(skizzirt 1841 neu instrumentirt 1851)' is crossed out on the first page of musical text; 'von neuem instrumentirt' appears on the last page of musical text; 'Skizzirt im J. 1841. Neu instrumentirt 1851' appears on the original title-page; 'Skizzirt im J. 1841, neu instrumentirt im J. 1853' appears on the new title-page added in 1853. There is no doubt that the 1841 MS formed the basis for the 1851 score; the early autograph contains corrections, additions, and annotations in Schumann's late handwriting, among them an instruction to a copyist to write out the Romanze and the Scherzo without expression marks ('ohne alle Vortragsbezeichnungen'); the expression marks

tentext, der über seine Sorgfalt hinaus auch Schumanns Ausdrucksart und seinen ästhetischen Standpunkt widerspiegelt. Das Fehlen einer Stichvorlage für die Partitur muß besonders bedauert werden. Ohne diese Handschrift sind die Abweichungen zwischen AUT und 1E schwerlich zu deuten. AUT stellt sich im Ausdruck wesentlich nuancierter dar als die „begradigte" 1E. Mit ziemlicher Sicherheit könnte die Stichvorlage als fehlendes Glied in der Kette für Anhaltspunkte dafür sorgen, was während des Kopierens an Feinheiten verlorenging und was Ergebnis von Verlagspolitik bzw. – gewohnheit war. (Aufgrund anderer Stichvorlagen von Kopistenhand müßte das Autograph zahlreiche Änderungen Schumanns enthalten; viele, wenn nicht alle ausdrucksbezogenen Vorschriften trügen seine Handschrift.)

Auch die Begleitumstände bei der Entstehung der Sinfoniefassung von 1851 erschweren es sehr, einen entgültigen Notentext zu erstellen. Die neue Partitur (AUT) entstand in nur acht Tagen vom 12. bis 19. Dezember 1851, auch für einen in der Regel zügig fortschreitenden Komponisten eine knappe Zeit. Schumann hat den Schwerpunkt offenbar auf Instrumentierung gesetzt, nachdem er sich nun schon auf die Überarbeitung eingelassen hatte. Er hat sich in AUT sogar mehrmals auf die Partitur von 1841 als eine Skizze bezogen: So strich er „(skizzirt 1841 neu instrumentirt 1851)" auf der ersten Notenseite durch; „von neuem instrumentirt" liest man auf der letzten Notenseite, „Skizzirt im J. 1841. Neu instrumentirt 1851" auf dem ursprünglichen Titelblatt, „Skizzirt im J. 1841, neu instrumentirt im J. 1853" auf dem 1853 hinzugekommenen Titelblatt. Zweifellos war die Partitur von 1841 Grundlage für die von 1851, denn die frühere zeigt Veränderungen, Verbesserungen und Bemerkungen in Schumanns Handschrift fortgeschrittener Tage. Dazu gehören die Anweisungen an den Kopisten, Romanze und Scherzo „ohne

in the Romanze and the Scherzo in AUT are in Schumann's hand, as are the brass and timpani parts and the bass line, which Schumann rewrote in 1851; the rest of the musical text of these movements is in the hand of the leader of the Düsseldorf orchestra, Wilhelm Joseph von Wasielewski.[19]

Many writers have discussed the differences between the 1841 and 1851 versions of the symphony,[20] but one significant issue has been largely ignored: are the notation (in particular the motoric re-barring of the outer movements), the intensified dynamic structure and accentuation, and the heavy orchestration of the 1851 version appropriate to the essentially unchanged style of the music composed 10 years earlier?

alle Vortragsbezeichnungen" abzuschreiben; dazu gehören seine Vortragsbezeichnungen in Romanze und Scherzo von AUT für Blechbläser, Pauken und Baßgruppe, die er 1851 umschrieb; und die Tatsache, daß Wilhelm Joseph von Wasiliewski, Konzertmeister des Düsseldorfer Orchesters, die Abschrift dieser Sätze zuende führte.[19]

Zahlreiche Autoren haben die Unterschiede der Sinfonie-Fassungen von 1841 und 1851 diskutiert[20], doch ein bezeichnendes Resultat ist weitgehend übersehen worden: Sind Notation (besonders die motorische Neu-Balkung in den Ecksätzen), intensivierte dynamische Struktur und Akzentsetzung sowie die „schwere" Instrumentierung der Fassung von 1851 dem in den Grundzügen unveränderten, zehn Jahre

---

[19] See Renate Federhofer-Königs, 'Wilhelm Joseph von Wasiliewski, Schumanns Düsseldorfer Konzertmeister und Biograph', Robert Schumann – Ein romantisches Erbe in neuer Forschung, ed. Robert-Schumann-Gesellschaft (Mainz, 1984), P. 71. Wasiliewski's claim in his 1897 memoirs that the string parts throughout the 1851 score of the symphony are written in his hand is undoubtedly a lapse of memory; see Wilhelm Joseph von Wasiliewski, Aus siebzig Jahren (Stuttgart and Leipzig, 1897) p. 117. Positive identification of Wasiliewski's hand in the Romanze and the Scherzo was achieved by comparing the copyist's hand in the 1851 autograph with several bars of music in a Wasiliewski letter (copy in the Robert-Schumann-Forschungsstelle, Düsseldorf).

[20] Gerald Abraham, 'Three Scores of Schumann's D Minor Symphony', The Musical Times, 81 (1940), pp. 105–109, reprinted in Slavonic and Romantic Music (New York, 1968), pp. 281–287; Marc Andreae, 'Die vierte Symphonie Robert Schumanns, ihre Fassungen, ihre Interpretationsprobleme', Robert Schumann – Ein romantisches Erbe in neuer Forschung, ed. Robert-Schumann-Gesellschaft (Mainz, 1984), pp. 35–41; Mosco Carner, 'The Orchestral Music', Schumann: A Symposium, ed. Gerald Abraham (London, 1952), pp. 214–219; Jon William Finson, Robert Schumann: The Creation of the Symphonic Works, Ph.D. Diss., University of Chicago, 1980, pp. 214–242; Maria Rika Maniates, 'The D Minor Symphony of Robert Schumann', Festschrift für Walter Wiora zum 30. Dezember 1966, ed. Ludwig Finscher and Christoph-Hellmut Mahling (Kassel, 1967), pp. 441–447; Asher G. Zlotnik, 'Die beiden Fassungen von Schumanns d-moll-Symphonie', Österreichische Musikzeitschrift, 21 (1966), pp. 271–276.

[19] vgl. Renate Federhofer-Königs, „Wilhelm Joseph von Wasiliewski, Schumanns Düsseldorfer Konzertmeister und Biograph", in: Robert Schumann – Ein romantisches Erbe in neuer Forschung, hg. von der Robert-Schumann-Gesellschaft, Mainz 1984, S. 71. Wasiliewskis Behauptung in seinen Erinnerungen von 1897, er habe die Streicherstimmen der Sinfoniefassung von 1851 komplett eigenhändig abgeschrieben, ist zweifellos ein Gedächtnisfehler; vgl. Wilhelm Joseph von Wasiliewski, Aus siebzig Jahren, Stuttgart und Leipzig 1897, S. 117. Ein positiver Befund für Wasiliewskis Handschrift in Romanze und Scherzo ließ sich durch einen Vergleich der Kopistenhandschrift von 1851 mit einigen Takten eines Wasiliewski-Briefes ermitteln (Kopie in der Robert-Schumann-Forschungsstelle, Düsseldorf).

[20] Gerald Abraham, „The Three Scores of Schumann's D Minor Symphony", in: The Musical Times 81 (1940), S. 105–109, Reprint in: Slavonic and Romantic Music, New York 1968, S. 281–287; Marc Andreae, „Die vierte Symphonie Robert Schumanns, ihre Fassungen, ihre Interpretationsprobleme", in: Schumann – Ein romantisches Erbe, a. a. O., S. 35–41; Mosco Carner, „The Orchestral Music" in: Schumann: A Symposium, hg. von Gerald Abraham, London 1952, S.214–219; Jon William Finson, Robert Schumann: The Creation of the Symphonic Works, Diss., University of Chicago 1980, S. 214–242; Maria Rika Maniates, „The D Minor Symphony of Robert Schumann", in: Festschrift für Walter Wiora zum 30. Dezember 1966, ed. Ludwig Finscher und Christoph-Hellmut Mahling, Kassel 1967, S. 441–447; Asher G. Zlotnik, „Die beiden Fassungen von Schumanns d-moll-Symphonie", in: Österreichische Musikzeitschrift 21 (1966), S. 271–276

One of the most significant aspects of Schumann's music is that its subtleties of notation so acutely project its substance. The greater measure of 'personality' that emerges in works engraved from an autograph *Stichvorlage* (e.g., the scores of the first editions of Symphonies Nos. 2 and 3, Op. 61 and Op. 97) as compared with works engraved from a copyist's MS (e.g., the score of the first edition of Symphony No. 1, Op. 38) is intangible but real. It encompasses every detail, from beaming patterns to the placement of dynamics. When the degree of depersonalization caused by a copyist's capricious changes in notation is later compounded by a publisher's apparently inflexible house style, the composer's original intentions recede further into the background. These issues must be borne in mind when approaching the D minor symphony. In this instance the work in its 'final' (i.e., published) form is twice removed from the composer's 1851 autograph, which itself is a decade removed from the notation that most vividly reflects the style of the music.

There is little evidence in Schumann's diaries or correspondence to suggest that he spent much time preparing the symphony for publication or reading proofs. By 1853 the composer apparently had such a good working relationship with Breitkopf & Härtel[21] that he entrusted them with many of the editorial decisions and proof-reading chores he would have undertaken himself earlier in his career. It may well be that he attached less importance to the subtleties of notation in his later years (this question awaits further study). In any event, in view of the circumstances, the first edition – both 1E and OP – must be singled out as the only

vorher komponierten Werk eigentlich noch gemäß? Einer der bezeichnendsten Aspekte von Schumanns Musik zeigt sich in den Feinheiten der Notation, die so klar ihre Substanz widerspiegelt. Nicht greifbar, aber real ist der größere Anteil an Persönlichkeit, der in den Werken zum Vorschein kommt, die nach einer autographen Stichvorlage hergestellt wurden (z. B. die Erstausgaben der 2. und 3. Sinfonie op. 61 bzw. 97), im Vergleich mit denen, die nach einer Kopistenabschrift entstanden (beispielsweise die Erstausgabe der 1. Sinfonie op. 38). Er schließt jedes Detail von der Balkensetzung bis zur Position dynamischer Zeichen ein. Wenn dann noch zur Entpersönlichung der Notation durch Änderungen eines Kopisten die offenbar sturen Hausregeln eines Verlegers hinzukommen, werden die ursprünglichen Absichten eines Komponisten weiter verwässert. Man muß all diese Vorgaben im Hinterkopf haben, wenn man an die d-Moll-Sinfonie herangeht. In diesem Fall ist das Werk in seiner letzten, d. h. veröffentlichten Form zwei Schritte vom Autograph des Komponisten aus dem Jahre 1851 entfernt, und dieses wiederum ein Jahrzehnt von einer Niederschrift, die so lebendig das Spezifische der Komposition wiedergibt.

In Schumanns Tagebüchern oder sonstiger Korrespondenz gibt es kaum Hinweise darauf, er hätte viel Zeit mit den Vorbereitungen zur Drucklegung oder zum Korrekturlesen verbracht. Um 1853 bestand zwischen Schumann und Breitkopf & Härtel offenbar eine so gute Geschäftsbeziehung,[21] daß er dem Verlag in vielen Editionsfragen und dem Tagesgeschäft des Korrekturlesens sein Vertrauen schenkte – in Dingen, die er früher in seiner Laufbahn selbst erledigt hätte. Gut möglich, daß er in seinen letzten Jahren den Feinheiten seiner Notation nicht mehr so viel Aufmerksamkeit schenkte (in diesem Punkt ist weiterge-

[21] See Kurt Hofmann, *Die Erstdrucke der Werke von Robert Schumann* (Tutzing, 1979), pp. ix–xi

[21] vgl. Kurt Hofmann, *Die Erstdrucke der Werke von Robert Schumann*, Tutzing 1979, S. ix–xi

feasible text upon which to base the present edition. The edition largely follows IE, which has fewer errors and inconsistencies than OP. However, the reading of OP has been followed in instances where the placement of dynamic indications is more accurate, and in the phrasing of second wind parts, which are sometimes left unphrased or only partially phrased in IE (where pairs of instruments share staves). The reading of AUT has been followed at several major points of articulation in the symphony where it was felt that the additional indications of nuance – possibly also present in the missing *Stichvorlage* – may have been incompatible with the house style of Breitkopf & Härtel and therefore omitted from IE. The following may be cited as an example. In AUT, Schumann wrote the final *sforzando* in both outer movements as: *sfz*. He appears to have been in the habit of writing *sfz*, as opposed to *sf*, when he wanted a somewhat stronger accent, the 'z' visually communicating this added stress. In MSS dating from all periods of his life, Schumann differentiates between *sfz* and *sf* (often *sfz* is even written larger than *sf*). Since *sfz* is used sparingly in the 1851 autograph of the D minor symphony – it is found only in the two places cited above – the nuance in emphasis that it conveys should not be omitted from the musical text of the symphony.

The rehearsal letters in the present edition are Schumann's and appear in AUT, IE, and OP. The parentheses enclosing Schumann's metronome markings appear in IE, but not in other sources.

Obvious engraver's errors in the printed sources have been corrected without comment.

Linda Correll Roesner

hende Forschung vonnöten). Wie dem auch sei: Mit Blick auf die Umstände der Erstausgabe schälen sich zwangsläufig IE und OP als einzig mögliche Vorlage für diese Ausgabe heraus. Sie lehnt sich weitgehendst an IE an, weil es weniger Fehler und Unstimmigkeiten als OP in sich birgt. Andererseits wurde der Lesart von OP der Vorzug gegeben, wenn dynamische Bezeichnungen hier genauer waren oder IE die zweiten Bläserstimmen bei der Notierung in nur einem System gar nicht oder nur unvollständig phrasierte. AUT war dann maßgeblich bei mehreren wichtigen Fragen der Artikulation, wenn der Eindruck entstand, die zusätzlichen detaillierten Hinweise – die womöglich auch in der Stichvorlage gegeben waren – hätten gegen die Redaktionsrichtlinien von Breitkopf & Härtel verstoßen und wären aus diesem Grund aus IE getilgt worden. Dazu ein Beispiel: In AUT notierte Schumann das abschließende *sforzando* in den Ecksätzen als *sfz*. Er hatte dem Anschein nach die Gewohnheit, *sfz* im Unterschied zu *sf* zu notieren, wenn er einen etwas stärkeren Akzent beabsichtigte, und diese Absicht vermittelt das „z" visuell. Zeitlebens hat Schumann in seinen Manuskripten einen Unterschied zwischen *sfz* und *sf* gemacht, und *sfz* ist oft größer geschrieben als *sf*. Da *sfz* im Autograph der d-Moll-Sinfonie von 1851 sparsam verwendet wird – und auch nur an den oben angeführten zwei Stellen anzutreffen ist –, darf dieses emphatische Detail nicht aus dem Notentext der Sinfonie entfernt werden.

Die Studierbuchstaben in dieser Ausgabe stammen von Schumanns Hand und sind aus AUT, IE und OP übernommen. Schumanns Metronomangaben in Klammern kommen außer in IE in keiner der Quellen vor.

Offensichtliche Stichfehler in den gedruckten Quellen wurden stillschweigend korrigiert.

Linda Correll Roesner
Übersetzung Norbert Henning

IE = First edition of the score
OP = First edition of the orchestral parts
AUT = Schumann's 1851 autograph score (The readings of AUT are reported only when AUT agrees with OP against IE, or when AUT has a significant variant reading.)

Br. = Brass
Str. = Strings
Ww. = Woodwind
b(b) = bar(s)
n(n) = note(s)

Ziemlich langsam – Lebhaft

bar 7–9 Cor. 1 c′ in OP

9 Vc., Cb. $\lessgtr$ centered on d in OP, AUT

12–14 Ob. slur from b12, n4 to b13, n3 and from b13, n4 to b14, n3 in OP, AUT

13 Vla., Vc. slur ends on c′ in OP, AUT

14 Vla., Vc. slur over nn1–3 in OP, AUT

16 Fg. 2 n3 d in OP (in AUT, n3 originally d; late correction to B flat)

17 Timp. *p* in OP

29, 33 Vc., Cb. > on n1 in OP

32 Vc., Cb. no stacc. on nn5–8 in OP, AUT

33 Tr. 1 a in AUT

37 Vc., Cb. no > on n1 in OP, AUT

39 Vl. I text of b38 repeated in AUT

42 Cl. 2 n1 b′ in AUT

42 Timp. stacc. dot on n1 in OP, AUT; Vc., Cb. stacc. dot on n1 in OP

43–44 Cl. slur from c′ to c″ sharp in OP, AUT

44 Fl., Ob. slur over entire bar in OP, AUT

45–46 Cl. slur from e′ to c″ sharp in OP

46 Fl., Ob. slur over entire bar in OP

47 Fg. 1 *p* follows OP

48 Vla., Vc. no stacc. on n3 in OP, AUT

55 Vc., Cb. slur from e flat to d in OP, AUT

55–56 Ob. 1 slur from f‴ to d″ flat in OP, AUT

55–56 Fg. 1 slur from f′ to d′ flat in OP, AUT

57 Ob. 1, Cl. 1 no *dolce* in AUT

83 Vl. I/II *f* in AUT (Vl. I/II), OP (Vl. II only)

87, 90 Tbn. *sf* ⇒ in OP

89, 92 Fl., Ob. slur from e″flat to c‴ in OP, AUT

101–117 Vl. I no stacc. dots throughout in OP; stacc. dots in bb105–106 and bb109–110 on AUT

117 Vla. no stacc. dots in OP, AUT

147 Vla., Vc., Cb. no *dolce* in OP, AUT

151 Cl. 1 *cresc.* follows OP

151 Fg. 1 *p* follows OP; *cresc.* by analogy with Fg. 2; Fg. 1 *dolce* in OP; Fg. 2 *dol.* in AUT

151 Vl. II placement of *cresc.* follows OP and AUT

160–162 Ob. 1 slur from e″ to f″ sharp in OP, AUT; no slur from f″ sharp to g″ sharp in AUT

164–165 Fg. 1 slur from c′ sharp to b natural in OP, AUT

166 Cl. 2 notated g′ natural in OP

167–168 Vl. I no *sf* in OP, AUT

171, 172 Cl. 2 n1 notated d′ natural in OP

171, 172 Cor. 1/2 notated d′ sharp in OP

173, 174 Cl. 2 n1 notated g′ natural in OP

175 Vl. I *sf* from OP, AUT, and by ananlogy with b101

175–188 Vl. I no stacc. dots throughout in OP, AUT

191 Vc., Cb. no *sf* in OP, *f* (in pencil) in AUT

194 Vl. I/II n7 notated g natural in OP, AUT

195–221 Tr. remains in F and notated for Tr. in F in OP

206 Vla., Vc., Cb. *sf* on n1 in OP

211, 213, 215 Ww. *sf* on n1 in OP, AUT

215 Vl. I ♪ ⁊ on beat 1 in OP, AUT

217, 219 Ww. *sf* on n1 in OP

221 Vla. no *dolce* in OP, AUT

230 Ww. *f* in OP, AUT

242, 245 Ww. *f* on beat 1 in OP, AUT

XVIII

265 Vc., Cb. *f* (instead of *sf*) on n1 in OP, AUT

265–296 Str. no stacc. dots on the semiquavers in OP, AUT

266 Vla. *f* (instead of *sf*) on n1 in OP

266–291 Ww. no stacc. dots on the semiquavers in AUT

311–313 All parts crescendo dashes follow AUT (see Editorial Notes)

325–326 Tbn. 1/2 slur in OP

329–330 Tbn. 1/2 slur in OP, AUT

333 Cl. 2 notated g′ natural in OP

336 Br. and Ww. *f* follows OP and AUT

337 Fg. n3 written as 2 semiquavers in AUT

337–348 Vl. I/II, Vla. no stacc. dots in OP, AUT

337–348 Fl., Ob., Cl. no stacc. dots in AUT

358 All parts *sf* in IE, OP; *sfz* follows AUT (see Editorial Notes)

Romanze

bar10, 24 Vla. *dolce* in OP

24–25 Vl. solo reads as Vl. I in OP

25 Vc. II *pp* in OP

34 Cb. ══ under n1 in IE; present reading follows OP and AUT

42¹ Cb. ◁══ by analogy with b34

42²–44 Vl. I/II, Vla., Vc. II articulation follows OP and AUT (IE: ♪ ۷ | ♪ ۷ , etc.)

Scherzo

bar 1 Ob. 1, Vl. I no *sf* in OP, AUT

24–32, Vl. I/II no stacc. dots in OP, AUT
136–144

38–39 Cl. 1 tie from d′ to d′ in IE, OP, AUT; present articulation by analogy with Ob., Fg.
151–152

49 Vl. I no *sf* in OP, AUT

69 Fg. 2 *dol.* in OP

93 Vla. I *p* by analogy with Vla. II

113 Fl., Fg., Tr. *f* from OP and by analogy with b1

113 Ob., Cl., Cor. Timp., Str. *f* by analogy with b1

203–204 Cor. 2 $\Longleftrightarrow$ by analogy with bb91–92 (Cor. 1) and all other parts

225 Vla. I *pp* by analogy with Vla. II

Langsam – Lebhaft

bar 3 Cor. 1/2, Tbn. *cresc.* follows OP

7, 14 Vl. II/1 *cresc.* follows Vl. II/2

11 Tbn. 2 $\wedge$ follows OP

12 Vl. II/1 *p* follows Vl. II/2

14 Ob. stacc. dot on n12 by analogy with other Ww.

17–20 Vla., Vc., Cb. no stacc. dots in OP, AUT

38 Str. placement of *dim.* follows OP and AUT

46 Ob. 2, Cl. 2 $\diminuendo$ in OP

48, 50 Fl. 2, Ob. 2, Cl. 2 $\diminuendo$ in OP

52 Ob. 1 *dim.* by analogy with Fl. 1 in OP

53 Cl. 1 *p* follows OP

54 Fl. 1 *p* folloes OP

68, 70 Vl. II no $\wedge$ on the minim in OP, AUT

69 Vc., Cb. no *f* in OP, AUT

73–74 Timp. tie bb73–74 n1 in 1E, OP; present reading follows AUT

73, 74 Vl. II/1 no a′ (b73, beat 3; b74, beat 1) in OP, AUT

79 Cor. 3/4, Tr. footnote in 1E, OP: 'Diese, später wiederholte *sf* müssen von den Blasinstrumentalisten durch wachsende Kraft der Brust hervorgebracht werden'.

82 Fg. placement of *sf p* follows OP and AUT

82 Vc. placement of *sf p* following AUT and by analogy with Fg. (OP, AUT)

85 Ob., Vla. placement of *sf p* by analogy with Fg., b82 (OP, AUT)

88 Cl., Vl. II placement of *sf p* by analogy with Fg., b82 (OP, AUT)

88 Vl. I *sfp* in 1E; *sf* in OP; present reading follows AUT

91 Fl., Vl. I placement of *sf p* by analogy with Fg., b82 (OP, AUT)

101–102 Timp. $\overset{tr}{}$ in OP, AUT; ditto bb102–103, 103–104, 111–112, 113–114

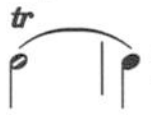

106 Cl. 1 *f* by analogy with Cl. 2

110 Fg. 1 *f* follows OP

110–112 Tbn. 3 *f* in b110 in IE, OP, AUT; *sf* in bb110–112 by analogy with Vc., Cb., Fg. 2

111 Cl. *f* follows OP (*sf* – in Cl. 2 only – in IE)

112 Cl. 2 *sf* on n2 in IE; present reading follows OP and AUT

121 Vla. I *p* by analogy with Vla. II

123 Fg. 1 *cresc.* by analogy with Fg. 2

123 Vla. I *cresc.* by analogy with Vla. II

124 Fg. *cresc.* in OP

131 Ob. 1, Cl. 1 *p* from OP (Ob. 1) and by analogy with b43 (placement of *p* in IE ambiguous)

131 Cl. 1/2 > on minim in IE (Cl. 1) and OP (Cl. 2)

142 Ob. 1 *dim.* by analogy with all other parts

143 Ob. 1, Cl. 2, Fg. 1, Vl. I > by analogy with b54 (Fl. 1, Ob. 1, Vla.)

148 Vl. II/1 ⟨⟩ by analogy with Vl. II/2

169, 171 Timp. tie from nn1–2 in OP

176–177 Timp. tie from minim to crotchet in OP
184–185

188 Tbn. *f* on beat 1 in OP

192 Fl. 1 *sf* by analogy with Fl. 2 and all other parts

206–207 Vl. I 'General-Pausen' in OP

208 Vl. I *ff* in OP, AUT (instead of *ff* on last quaver of b207)

234 All parts *sf* in IE, OP; *sfz* follows AUT (see Editorial Notes)

Linda Correll Roesner

Orchestration/Orchesterbesetzung

Flauto 1, 2
Oboe 1, 2
Clarinetto 1, 2
Fagotto 1, 2
Corno 1–4
Tromba 1, 2
Trombone 1–3
Timpani
Violino I, II
Viola
Violoncello
Contrabasso

SYMPHONY No. 4

Robert Schumann
(1810–1856)
Op. 120

Ziemlich langsam (♩ =52)

Flauto 1 2

Oboe 1 2

Clarinetto (B♭) 1 2

Fagotto 1 2

Corno (F) 1 2

(D) 3 4

Tromba (F) 1 2

Alto Tenore Trombone 1 2

Basso 3

Timpani (D, A)

Violino I

II

Viola

Violoncello

Contrabasso

EE 6760

Edited by Linda Correll Roesner
© 1997 Ernst Eulenburg Ltd
and Ernst Eulenburg & Co GmbH

EE 6760

4

6

Lebhaft (♩ =92)

24

32

* B = deutsche H

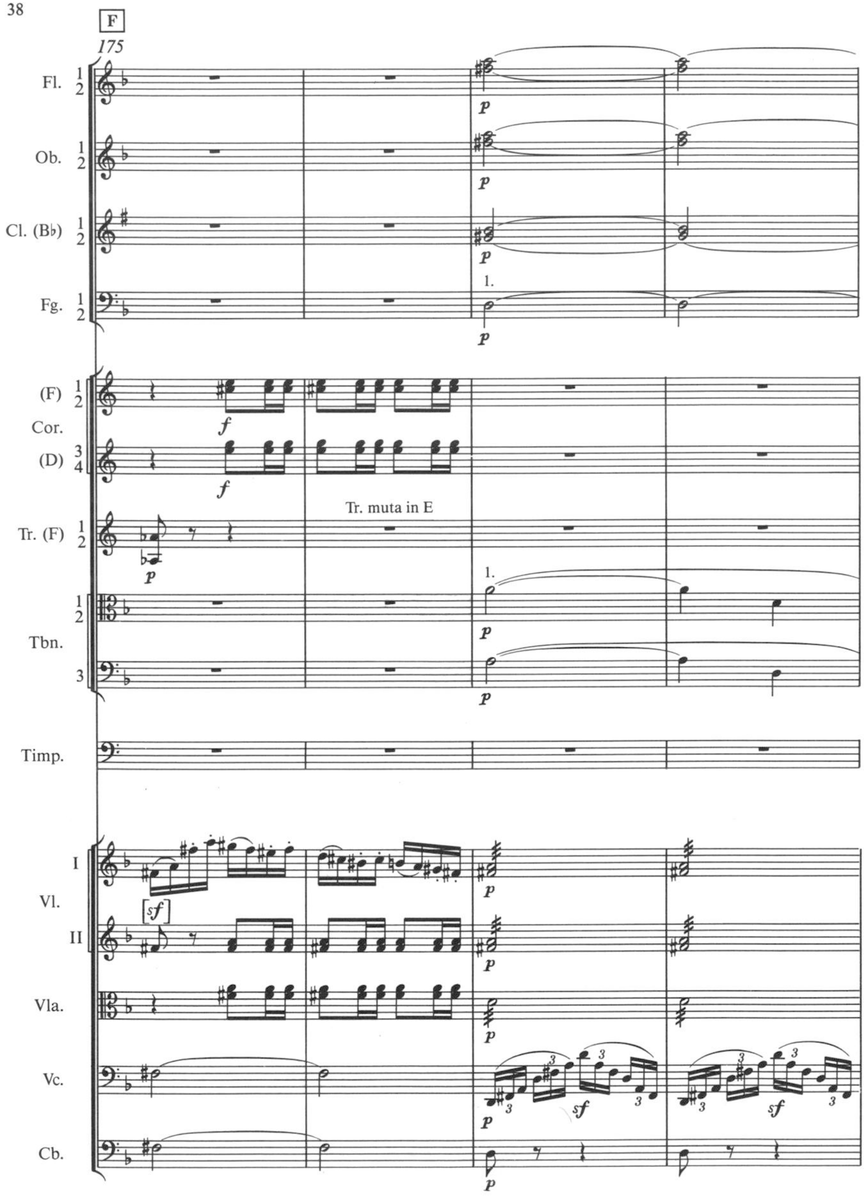
F
175
Fl.
Ob.
Cl. (B♭)
Fg.
(F)
Cor.
(D)
Tr. (F)
Tr. muta in E
Tbn.
Timp.
I
Vl.
II
Vla.
Vc.
Cb.

48

EE 6760

EE 6760

68

70

EE 6760

Romanze

Ziemlich langsam (♩ =66)

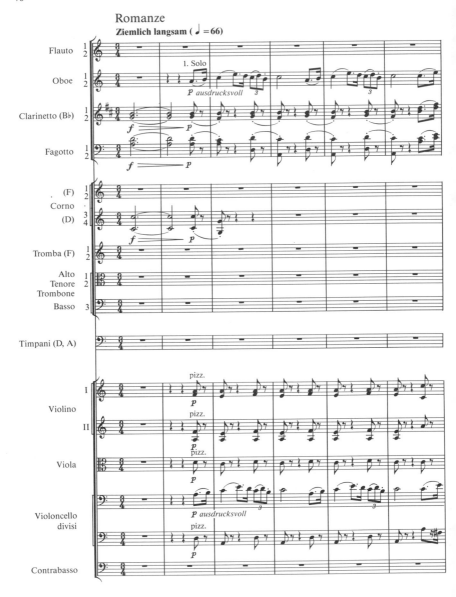

EE 6760

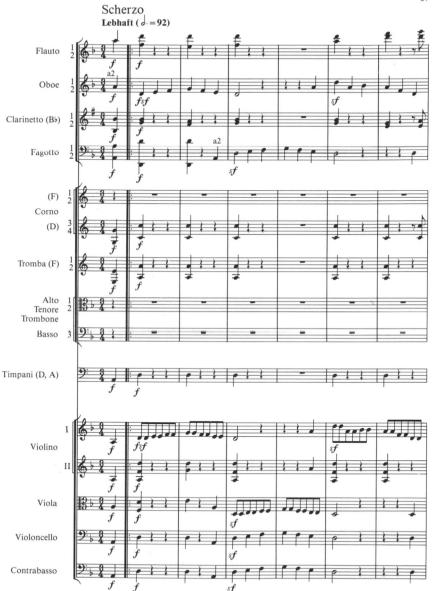

EE 6760

53
1
Fl. 1 2
Ob. 1 2
sf
Cl. (B♭) 1 2
Fg. 1 2
sf
(F) 1 2
Cor.
(D) 3 4
a2
Tr. (F) 1 2
Tbn. 1 2
3
Timp.
I
Vl.
II
sf
Vla.
sf
Vc.
sf
Cb.
sf

Trio

100

EE 6760

102

EE 6760

110

112

118

124

EE 6760

128

EE 6760

EE 6760

142

EE 6760

Schneller

EE 6760

172

EE 6760